Logic Decimal Problems

Wade H. Sherard III

Dale Seymour Publications®
White Plains, New York

Special recognition and thanks are due to those middle school and high school teachers and their students in the School District of Greenville County and the Pickens County School District who tested the puzzles in this collection and to Michele C. Fray for all of her help and expertise in preparing this manuscript for publication.

Managing Editor: Catherine Anderson
Senior Editor: John Nelson
Production/Manufacturing Director: Janet Yearian
Production/Manufacturing Coordinator: Joan Lee
Design Director: Phyllis Aycock
Cover and Interior Illustrations: Corbin Hillam
Text Design: Elaine Lopez
Composition: Claire Flaherty
Cover Design: Elaine Lopez

This book is published by Dale Seymour Publications®,
an imprint of Addison Wesley Longman, Inc.

Dale Seymour Publications
10 Bank Street
White Plains, NY 10602
Customer Service: 800-872-1100

Order number 21885
ISBN 0-7690-0082-7

1 2 3 4 5 6 7 8 9 10-ML-02 01 00 99 98

This Book Is Printed
on Recycled Paper

INTRODUCTION

Logic Decimal Problems is a collection of 54 decimal number puzzles designed to provide experiences in problem solving and mathematical reasoning for middle school and high school students. Each puzzle consists of a sequence of ten clues about an unknown decimal number. The clues, when revealed one at a time, lead students through deductive reasoning to the discovery of the unknown decimal number. Because students need to know only basic definitions, concepts, and properties from numeration, number theory, and the arithmetic of fractions, decimals, and percents to solve the puzzles, the primary emphasis is on problem-solving strategies and mathematical reasoning.

Learning to solve problems is one of the most important reasons for students at all levels to study mathematics. Critical-thinking and reasoning skills developed through problem-solving activities in mathematics are useful in solving problems in many different disciplines. Consequently, the curriculum is placing greater emphasis on teaching problem solving and mathematical reasoning. In spite of this emphasis, however, assessment studies show that students' problem-solving abilities are still considerably weaker than their computational abilities. Clearly, more work needs to be done to improve students' abilities to solve problems, to reason mathematically, and to think critically.

The work of George Polya has been a dominant influence on the teaching of problem solving in mathematics. Polya recommends a four-phase procedure to provide structure and guidance in solving a problem.

Phase I: Understanding the Problem
Phase II: Devising a Plan
Phase III: Carrying Out the Plan
Phase IV: Looking Back

Polya discusses these four phases and suggestions for implementing them in detail in his books *How to Solve It* (first published in 1945) and *Mathematical Discovery.** These books have had a tremendous impact on the teaching of problem solving. Analyses of articles, books, and current mathematics curricula concerning problem solving reveal many of Polya's ideas, especially these four phases for solving a problem.

The second of Polya's phases, devising a plan, is probably the most difficult for students. The following strategies for this phase (most of which are directly attributable to Polya) are especially appropriate for solving the decimal number puzzles in this collection.

1. Make a list of possibilities. Can the list be modified or reduced, given the conditions of the problem?

2. Carefully consider the conditions of the problem. What new information can be derived from the conditions? Are all the conditions necessary? Have all the conditions been taken into account?

3. Think of a related problem or situation. Are there definitions or properties that are related to the unknowns, the data, and the conditions of the problem?

4. Consider a similar problem. Can its method of solution be used?

5. Search for patterns in the conditions or data. Is there a pattern that may be useful?

6. Try a guess-and-test approach; that is, an organized, systematic procedure of trial and error.

---

*Polya, George. *How to Solve It,* 2nd ed. (Princeton, NJ: Princeton University Press, 1973); *Mathematical Discovery,* combined edition. (New York: John Wiley & Sons, 1981).

The puzzles in this collection provide students with ample opportunities to develop and use these problem-solving strategies.

The fourth of Polya's phases, looking back, is probably the most neglected phase in the teaching of problem solving, and it needs to be emphasized. The following are key questions for students to ask during this phase.

1. Is the answer reasonable? Does it make sense? Does the solution meet all the conditions of the problem? Can the solution be checked?

2. Is there another method for solving the problem? Is it shorter or more efficient? Is there another pattern of reasoning that leads to the solution?

3. Is the method of solution useful for solving other problems? Should the method of solution be remembered?

The puzzles in this collection provide students with many opportunities to ask these phase-four questions.

Polya insists that the teaching of problem solving must include abundant experience in solving specific problems as well as careful study of the solution process itself. Students who solve, or attempt to solve, puzzles in this collection will gain valuable experience in solving problems and, with appropriate guidance from their teacher, will begin to study the general process of problem solving.

Below are the basic definitions, concepts, and properties students need to know to solve these puzzles. These fundamental ideas from numeration, number theory, and the arithmetic of fractions, decimals, and percents are part of the standard curriculum for middle school mathematics.

Numeration

- concepts of place value and face value
- comparison of decimal numbers using face values and place values of their numerals
- patterns in the digits of a decimal numeral
- locating the decimal point in a decimal numeral

Number Theory

- even and odd numbers
- divisors, factors, and multiples of numbers
- prime numbers and composite numbers
- prime factors of numbers
- greatest common divisors and least common multiples
- square numbers and cubic numbers
- palindromes

Arithmetic of Fractions, Decimals, and Percents

- equivalences among fractions, decimals, and percents
- multiplication by fractions, decimals, and percents
- ratios
- vocabulary related to addition, subtraction, multiplication, and division as operations
- properties of the number 0 with respect to addition, subtraction, and multiplication
- properties of the number 1 with respect to multiplication and division
- square roots

The puzzles in this collection provide opportunities for students to develop a better understanding of decimals and the relationships among fractions, decimals, and percents; to reinforce their understanding of place value and face value in numeration; to learn important vocabulary related to computation; and to develop their skills in making and recognizing patterns. Solving these puzzles helps students develop number sense while they are developing skills in solving problems and reasoning mathematically. In addition, many of the clues of the puzzles expose students to the language of algebra.

Sample Puzzles and Suggested Solutions

Each decimal number puzzle in this collection consists of a list of ten clues. The clues are designed to be disclosed one at a time, with each new clue providing more information about the unknown decimal number. The objective of the puzzle is to discover the unknown decimal number by using the least possible number of clues. The clues allow students to use deductive reasoning to determine the various digits of its numeral as well as the location of its decimal point and thus the unknown number. Once the number has been determined, the remaining clues in the list serve to confirm the solution. Solutions to the 54 puzzles in this book can be found on page 55. The following conditions hold for each decimal number that is the solution to a puzzle in this collection:

- Each decimal number is a positive number.

- If the decimal number is less than 1, its numeral must be written with a 0 in ones place. For example, if the number is seventy-five hundredths, its numeral must be written 0.75, not .75.

- It is appropriate for the last digit of the decimal number to be 0, if the clues require that the digit in the last place value be 0.

Below are three sample puzzles and suggested solutions.

Puzzle A

1. It is a five-digit decimal number.

2. It is less than 40%.

3. Its tenths digit is one-half of its thousandths digit.

4. The sum of its hundredths digit and its ten-thousandths digit is 1.

5. It is less than $\frac{1}{5}$.

6. Its thousandths digit is a prime number.

7. Its tenths digit and its hundredths digit are the same.

8. The sum of all of its digits is 4.

9. It is close to 11%.

10. Its ten-thousandths digit is 0.

Suggested Solution to Puzzle A by Clues:

1. The decimal number has the form __ __ __ __ __ without its decimal point.

2. This clue locates the decimal point and restricts the possible digits for tenths place.

```
        3
        2
        1
  0     0
  __ . __ __ __ __
```

3. The possible digits for thousandths place are 0, 2, 4, and 6, respectively.

```
        3           6
        2           4
        1           2
  0     0           0
  __ . __ __ __ __
```

4. Either the hundredths digit is 0 and the ten-thousandths digit is 1, or vice versa.

```
        3           6
        2           4
        1    1      2    0
  0     0    0      0    1
  __ . __ __ __ __
```

1, 2, 3, 4. Collectively, these clues allow us to make the following brief list of possible numbers:

0.0001	0.1021	0.2041	0.3061
0.0100	0.1120	0.2140	0.3160

5. The list is now reduced to

0.0001	0.1021
0.0100	0.1120

6. The list is further reduced to

0.1021

0.1120

7. The unknown decimal number must be 0.1120.

v

8, 9, 10. These conditions serve to confirm that 0.1120 is the solution to the puzzle.

Several problem-solving strategies from Polya's second phase, devising a plan, are used to solve Puzzle A. The underlying strategy is that of making a list of possibilities. The new information revealed with each clue allows students to continue to reduce the list of possibilities until the solution is easily determined. The conditions in the clues require students to consider definitions, concepts, or properties related to the unknown decimal number. Using patterns is an important problem-solving strategy in generating the brief list of possible decimal numbers that satisfy the first four clues. Patterns help ensure that a systematic search is made to find all possible numbers satisfying the clues. This prevents a haphazard, trial-and-error approach that may well overlook potential candidates for the solution—a good point to discuss in the looking-back phase of this puzzle's solution.

Not all of the clues are needed to solve Puzzle A. The solution can be determined after clue 7. The remaining clues can be used to confirm the solution. After solving this or any other puzzle, it is important for students to ask the following questions: Is this answer reasonable? Does it make sense? Can the method of solution be used to solve other problems? Is there another way to derive the solution? These questions begin Polya's fourth phase, looking back, a reflection on the puzzle's solution.

Puzzle B

1. It is a four-digit decimal number.

2. The quotient of its ones digit and its thousandths digit is 1.

3. Its hundredths digit is even.

4. None of its digits are prime numbers.

5. Its tenths digit is 25% of its hundredths digit.

6. It is less than 500%.

7. The product of all of its digits is 64.

8. Each of its digits is a square number.

9. Three of its digits are the same.

10. Its thousandths digit is 4.

Suggested Solution to Puzzle B by Clues:

1. The decimal number has the form
   _ _ _ _ without its decimal point.

2. Since there are only four place values, this clue locates the decimal point and determines that ones digit and thousandths digit must be the same nonzero number.

3, 4. The digits must be 0, 1, 4, 6, 8, or 9, and the hundredths digit in particular must be 0, 4, 6, or 8. The decimal number must now have the form

9			9
8		8	8
6		6	6
4		4	4
1		0	1
_	.	_	_	_

5. If its hundredths digit is 0, its tenths digit is 0. Or if its hundredths digits is 4, its tenths digit is 1. At this point, the decimal number has the form

9				9
8				8
6				6
4	1		4	4
1	0		0	1
_	.	_	_	_

The list of possible decimal numbers satisfying the first five clues is

1.001	4.004	6.006	8.008	9.009
1.141	4.144	6.146	8.148	9.149

6. The list is now reduced to

1.001	4.004
1.141	4.144

7. The unknown number must be 4.144.

8, 9, 10. These conditions serve to confirm that 4.144 is the solution to the puzzle.

As with Puzzle A, the key problem-solving strategy in devising a plan for Puzzle B is that of making a list of possibilities and reducing the list based on the clues. Looking for patterns in the digits of decimal numbers is important again to ensure that the list of possible solutions after the fifth clue is complete.

Puzzle C

1. It is a six-digit decimal number.

2. It is greater than 10 but less than 100.

3. Its tens digit is a multiple of 7.

4. The least common multiple of its tenths digit and its hundredths digit is 12.

5. The ratio of its hundredths digit to its thousandths digit is 1:2.

6. Its ones digit is the greatest common divisor of its tens digit and its thousandths digit.

7. Its ten-thousandths digit is the sum of its ones digit and its hundredths digit.

8. Each of its digits is different.

9. It has more odd digits than even digits.

10. Its thousandths digit is 8.

Suggested Solution to Puzzle C by Clues:

1. The decimal number has the form
   _ _ _ _ _ _ without its
   decimal point.

2. This clue locates the decimal point since the whole number portion of the decimal number must be a two-digit number.

3. The tens digit must be 7.

4. Either the tenths digit is 3 and the hundredths digit is 4, or vice versa.

5. If the hundredths digit is 3, then the thousandths digit is 6. Or if the hundredths digit is 4, then the thousandths digit is 8. At this point, the decimal number has the form

			4	3	6
7			3	4	8

_ _ . _ _ _ _

6. The ones digit must be 1.

7. At this point the list of possible decimal numbers is

    71.3485

    71.4364

8. The unknown decimal number must be 71.3485.

9, 10. These conditions serve to confirm that 71.3485 is the solution to the puzzle.

According to Polya, students must have experience not only in solving problems but also in studying the process of solving problems. During Polya's fourth phase, looking back, students must reflect on their work and ask these questions: Can this method of solution be used to solve other puzzles? If so, should it be remembered? Is there another way to solve the puzzle? Is there a better method? A more efficient method?

Looking back gives students a basis for developing plans for solving other problems. When students are faced with a new problem, they can use what they have learned from looking back at the solutions to other problems to help them answer these questions: Have I solved a similar problem? Can the solution method from that problem be used to solve this problem? Many puzzles in this collection have similar structures for students to identify and then apply the appropriate solution strategies.

Algebraic Thinking

The puzzles in this book provide students with opportunities to engage in algebraic thinking. Algebra can be viewed as a language for expressing mathematical relationships. The language used in many of the clues about unknown digits and the relationships among them is the language of algebra. (The variables in a puzzle are the digits of the place values of the decimal number that is the solution to the puzzle.) Students engage in algebraic thinking when they use clues such as the following:

- The sum of its tenths digit and its thousandths digit is 7.

- The difference between its tens digit and its hundredths digit is 3.
- Its ones digit is a factor of 8.
- Its hundredths digit is one fourth of its ten-thousandths digit.
- Its tenths digit is less than its hundredths digit.

Clues such as these are the English equivalents of algebraic equations, inequalities, or expressions, and finding all possible digits that satisfy them involves algebraic thinking.

Several clues require students to apply algebraic properties of the numbers 0 and 1. For example, the clue, "The product of all of its digits is 0," requires students to conclude that at least one of the digits is 0. The clue, "The quotient of its ones digit and its tenths digit is 1," requires students to conclude that the ones digit and the tenths digit are the same nonzero digit. Both of these examples involve algebraic thinking.

Most of the puzzles require students to look for patterns, another aspect of algebraic thinking. For example, students may need to generate all possible numbers that satisfy the first several clues in a puzzle. To do this successfully, they must identify patterns that allow them to list systematically all the decimal numbers satisfying the information in those clues.

In solving these puzzles, students use their knowledge of numbers, number properties, and arithmetic to engage in algebraic thinking and to build meaning for the symbols and operations that they will learn later on when they study algebra more formally.

Suggestions for Using the Puzzles

The puzzles in this collection vary in difficulty. Some are straightforward and routine, while others are more challenging and thought-provoking, requiring greater creativity and insight. The more difficult puzzles appear in the latter part of the book. When deciding whether a particular puzzle is appropriate to use for a particular group of students, consider their mathematical background and level of achievement. Since the mathematical prerequisites for solving the puzzles are minimal, the puzzles are appropriate for most middle school and high school students.

The puzzles can be solved by students working individually or in small groups or teams. Since the objective of a puzzle is to determine the unknown decimal number by using the least number of clues, an assessment of students' work should be based not only on the solution's correctness but also on the number of clues used to find the solution. Of course, students must understand that the clues are to be disclosed one at a time and are to be considered sequentially.

The puzzles can be used in competitive game situations. For example, divide your class into teams of students, and uncover the clues to a puzzle one at a time using an overhead projector. When the students in a team think they have the solution to the puzzle, they can write it and the number of the last clue they used to determine it on a slip of paper; for example, 824.319, Clue 6. A possible scoring scheme is:
- + 1 for determining the unknown decimal number.
- + 2 for stating the number of the clue at which the solution can first be determined.
- + 1 for stating a clue number that is one greater than the clue number at which the solution number can first be determined.
- − 2 for stating an incorrect number (and for discouraging premature guessing).

If only a few teams are involved in the competition, points could also be awarded to the first team that determines the correct solution.

Regardless of how you use the puzzles, take time to discuss the solutions and the problem-solving strategies with your students. This important aspect of teaching problem solving will help students develop good problem-solving and reasoning skills. By providing careful, deliberate discussion of the problem-solving process, you can serve as a role model for students to emulate as they grow into successful problem solvers.

PUZZLE 1

1. It is a five-digit decimal number.

2. There are three places to the right of the decimal point.

3. Its tenths digit is $\frac{1}{5}$ of its tens digit.

4. Its hundredths digit is its smallest digit.

5. Each of its digits is different.

6. Its thousandths digit is an even prime number.

7. Its ones digit is the sum of all of its other digits.

8. Its thousandths digit is a factor of its ones digit.

9. Two of its digits are odd.

10. It is between 58 and 59.

PUZZLE 2

1. It is a four-digit decimal number.

2. It is greater than 0 but less than 1.

3. Its thousandths digit is a prime number.

4. Its tenths digit is three times its hundredths digit.

5. Its thousandths digit is its only odd digit.

6. It is greater than $\frac{3}{5}$.

7. Its hundredths digit is 3 less than its thousandths digit.

8. One of its digits is a 5.

9. Its smallest digit is 0.

10. It is equivalent to $\frac{5}{8}$.

PUZZLE 3

1. It is a four-digit decimal number.

2. Each of its digits is divisible by 3.

3. It is less than 10 but greater than 1.

4. Its tenths digit is its smallest digit.

5. Its thousandths digit is its largest digit.

6. Its ones digit is $\frac{2}{3}$ of its thousandths digit.

7. Each of its digits is different.

8. Its hundredths digit is a factor of its thousandths digit.

9. The product of all of its digits is 0.

10. Its tenths digit is 0.

PUZZLE 4

1. It is a six-digit decimal number.

2. It has only two different digits.

3. Its digits alternate.

4. It is less than 100 but greater than 10.

5. The quotient of its tenths digit and its thousandths digit is 1.

6. The quotient of two of its digits is 0.8.

7. Its hundredths digit is not divisible by 5.

8. Its ten-thousandths digit is even.

9. The product of all of its odd digits is 125.

10. Its ones digit is 4.

PUZZLE 5

1. It is a six-digit decimal number.

2. Each of its digits is a square number.

3. It is a palindrome.

4. Its hundredths digit is a divisor of each of its digits.

5. The least common multiple of its tenths digit and its thousandths digit is 36.

6. Its square root is greater than 30.

7. None of its digits is 0.

8. The sum of its thousandths digit and its tens digit is 10.

9. It is less than 1000.

10. Its tenths digit is 4.

PUZZLE 6

1. It is a five-digit decimal number.

2. Its largest place value is its ones place value.

3. Its ten-thousandths digit is twice its ones digit.

4. Its hundredths digit is $\frac{2}{3}$ of its ten-thousandths digit.

5. The product of its tenths digit and its thousandths digit is 1.

6. It has four different digits.

7. None of its digits are greater than 6.

8. The sum of all of its digits is 15.

9. It is close to π.

10. Its thousandths digit is 1.

PUZZLE 7

1. It is a five-digit decimal number.

2. Its ones digit is greater than the square root of 79.

3. The sum of its tenths digit and its hundredths digit is 6.

4. The sum of its hundredths digit and its thousandths digit is 5.

5. The sum of its thousandths digit and its ten-thousandths digit is 4.

6. The product of its tenths digit and its thousandths digit is 0.

7. Its ones digit is the sum of its hundredths digit and its ten-thousandths digit.

8. Two of its digits are divisible by 5.

9. It is greater than 9.15.

10. Its ten-thousandths digit is 4.

PUZZLE 8

1. It is a five-digit decimal number.

2. It is less than 200%.

3. It is greater than 100%.

4. None of its digits are the same.

5. Each digit is a divisor of the next digit to its right.

6. Its smallest digit is its ten-thousandths digit.

7. It has only one odd digit.

8. The product of all of its digits is 0.

9. It is less than 1.25.

10. Its ten-thousandths digit is 0.

PUZZLE 9

1. It is a five-digit decimal number.

2. Its ones digit is less than the square root of 2.

3. The product of its tenths digit and its hundredths digit is 24.

4. Its ten-thousandths digit is 1 less than its hundredths digit.

5. Its thousandths digit is $\frac{1}{2}$ of its hundredths digit.

6. The sum of all of its digits is 23.

7. Its hundredths digit is its largest digit.

8. It is less than 1.4142.

9. It has more odd digits than even digits.

10. Its ten-thousandths digit is 7.

PUZZLE 10

1. It is a four-digit decimal number.

2. Each of its digits is a square number.

3. Its tens digit and its ones digit are the same.

4. Its tenths digit and its hundredths digit are the same.

5. Its tens digit is $2\frac{1}{4}$ times greater than its hundredths digit.

6. Its tenths digit is 5 less than its ones digit.

7. The product of its ones digit and its hundredths digit is 36.

8. Its square root is less than 10.

9. None of its digits are zero.

10. Its tenths digit is 4.

PUZZLE 11

1. It is a six-digit decimal number.

2. It is a palindrome.

3. Its ones digit is $\frac{1}{3}$ of its hundredths digit.

4. The sum of its tens digit and its thousandths digit is 10.

5. The product of two of its digits is 1.

6. The sum of two of its digits is 8.

7. None of its digits are composite numbers.

8. The product of two of its digits is 49.

9. Two of its digits are divisible by 3.

10. Its tenths digit is 1.

PUZZLE 12

1. It is a four-digit decimal number.

2. It is less than 500%.

3. It is greater than 200%.

4. Its thousandths digit is twice its ones digit.

5. Its hundredths digit is 1 less than its thousandths digit.

6. The product of all of its digits is zero.

7. Three of its digits are not square numbers.

8. Three of its digits are divisible by 3.

9. The sum of all of its digits is 14.

10. Its hundredths digit is 5.

1.   It is a six-digit decimal number.

2.   Its smallest place value is its hundred-thousandths place.

3.   Each of its digits is 1 less than the digit to its right.

4.   Two of its digits are divisible by 4.

5.   Two of its digits are divisible by 3.

6.   Only one of its digits is a square number.

7.   Its hundredths digit is a prime number.

8.   Its hundred-thousandths digit is a composite number.

9.   It is greater than $\frac{5}{2}$.

10.   Its ten-thousandths digit is 7.

PUZZLE 14

1.   It is a five-digit decimal number.

2.   It is less than $\frac{7}{8}$.

3.   It is greater than $\frac{5}{6}$.

4.   None of its digits is an odd number.

5.   Its hundredths digit is not a factor of its tenths digit.

6.   Its tenths digit is a product of its thousandths digit and its ten-thousandths digit.

7.   It has two pairs of digits with a sum of 10.

8.   Its thousandths digit is its smallest nonzero digit.

9.   It is close to 86%.

10. Its ten-thousandths digit is 4.

PUZZLE 15

1. It is a five-digit decimal number.

2. Each of its digits is a cubic number.

3. It is less than 100%.

4. Its hundredths digit is the same as its ones digit.

5. It is greater than $\frac{4}{5}$.

6. The quotient of its thousandths digit and its ten-thousandths digit is 1.

7. It has only two different digits.

8. The product of any two of its digits is a square number.

9. Each of its digits is divisible by 8.

10. Its thousandths digit is 8.

PUZZLE 16

1. It is a four-digit decimal number.

2. Its largest place value is its ones place.

3. The squares of each of its digits are less than 9.

4. Its thousandths digit divided by its ones digit is 50%.

5. The sum of two of its digits is 0.

6. The difference between its ones digit and its thousandths digit is 1.

7. The sum of all of its digits is 3.

8. It has only one prime digit.

9. It is greater than 2.

10. Its tenths digit is 0.

PUZZLE 17

1. It is a four-digit decimal number.

2. Its tens digit has exactly one factor.

3. Its hundredths digit has exactly four factors.

4. Its tenths digit has exactly three factors.

5. The sum of two of its digits is 1.

6. The quotient of two of its digits is 0.5.

7. It has only one odd digit.

8. The product of two of its digits is twice 16.

9. It is less than 10.5.

10. Its hundredths digit is 8.

PUZZLE 18

1. It is a five-digit decimal number.

2. It is less than 1 but greater than 0.

3. Its hundredths digit is 80% of its tenths digit.

4. Its ten-thousandths digit is 25% of its hundredths digit.

5. Its thousandths digit is 1 more than its ten thousandths digit.

6. It is greater than $\frac{1}{2}$.

7. The difference between two of its digits is 2.

8. Its hundredths digit is a composite number.

9. Its ten-thousandths digit is its smallest nonzero digit.

10. Its tenths digit is 5.

PUZZLE 19

1. It is a five-digit decimal number.

2. Each of its digits is different.

3. It is greater than $\frac{6}{4}$ but less than $\frac{8}{5}$.

4. Its thousandths digit is its smallest digit.

5. Its ten-thousandths digit is 1 more than its hundredths digit.

6. Its hundredths digit is $\frac{7}{5}$ of its tenths digit.

7. The product of two of its digits is 56.

8. Two of its digits are divisible by 5.

9. Three of its digits are cubic numbers.

10. It is close to one half of π.

PUZZLE 20

1. It is a six-digit decimal number.

2. It has the same number of place values on either side of its decimal point.

3. Four of its digits are sevens.

4. The sum of its other two digits is 7.

5. None of its digits are composite numbers.

6. Only one of its digits is even.

7. Its hundredths digit is 40% of its tens digit.

8. The product of its hundreds digit and its thousandths digit is 49.

9. The product of its tens digit and its tenths digit is 35.

10. Its hundredths digit is 2.

PUZZLE 21

1. It is a six-digit decimal number.

2. It is greater than 100 but less than 1000.

3. The product of two of its digits is 1.

4. Its tenths digit is 60% of its hundredths digit.

5. Its ones digit is 40% of its hundredths digit.

6. Its ones digit is 25% of its thousandths digit.

7. The product of all of its digits is not 0.

8. Its thousandths digit is a composite number.

9. Its hundredths digit is the sum of its ones digit and its tenths digit.

10. Its tens digit is 1.

PUZZLE 22

1. It is an eight-digit decimal number.

2. Its digits are neither prime numbers nor composite numbers.

3. Its thousands digit and its ten-thousandths digit are the same.

4. The sum of all of its digits is 3.

5. Its ones digit is a factor of its ten-thousandths digit.

6. It is less than the square of 40.

7. It is greater than the cube of 10.

8. More than one half of its digits are 0.

9. The product of three of its digits is 1.

10. Its thousandths digit is 0.

PUZZLE 23

1. It is a six-digit decimal number.

2. Its hundredths digit is $\frac{1}{4}$ of its hundreds digit.

3. Its tenths digit is $\frac{1}{3}$ of its tens digit.

4. Its ones digit is $\frac{1}{5}$ of its thousandths digit.

5. None of its digits are 0.

6. The quotient of its tenths digit and its hundredths digit is 1.

7. The product of two of its digits is 48.

8. Its hundreds digit is its largest digit.

9. Only two of its digits are odd.

10. Its tens digit is 6.

PUZZLE 24

1. It is a six-digit decimal number.

2. The product of its ones digit and its thousands digit is 1.

3. The product of its hundredths digit and its thousands digit is 1.

4. The quotient of its hundreds digit and its tens digit is 1.

5. The product of two of its digits is 45.

6. The sum of four of its digits is 20.

7. Its tenths digit is its largest digit.

8. It has only three different digits.

9. Each of its digits is odd.

10. Its hundreds digit is 5.

PUZZLE 25

1.   It is a six-digit decimal number.

2.   There are three places to the left of the decimal point.

3.   The product of its hundreds digit and its tenths digit is 45.

4.   The least common multiple of its tens digit and its tenths digit is 45.

5.   The product of its ones digit and its tenths digit is 45.

6.   The least common multiple of its hundredths digit and its thousandths digit is 1.

7.   The greatest common divisor of its ones digit and its tenths digit is 1.

8.   Its tenths digit is greater than its tens digit.

9.   The product of three of its digits is 125.

10. Its tens digit is 5.

PUZZLE 26

1. It is a four-digit decimal number.

2. It is greater than $\frac{2}{3}$.

3. It is less than $\frac{3}{4}$.

4. It has only two different digits, each used twice.

5. Its tenths digit is the same as its thousandths digit.

6. The product of all of its digits is 0.

7. Its hundredths digit is the same as its ones digit.

8. The sum of all of its digits is 14.

9. It is greater than 70%.

10. It is less than 71%.

PUZZLE 27

1. It is a six-digit decimal number.

2. Its smallest place value is its thousandths place.

3. It has only three different digits.

4. The product of its hundreds digit and its hundredths digit is 1.

5. The product of its tenths digit and its hundredths digit is 0.

6. The sum of all of its digits is 6.

7. The least common multiple of its hundreds digit and its thousandths digit is 2.

8. The greatest common divisor of its ones digit and its thousandths digit is 2.

9. Its thousandths digit is the same as its ones digit.

10. Its hundredths digit is 1.

PUZZLE 28

1. It is a seven-digit decimal number.

2. Four of its digits are 0.

3. The face value of its smallest place value is 9.

4. Its other digits are prime numbers.

5. It is less than 1.

6. Its millionths digit is the sum of its ten-thousandths digit and its hundred-thousandths digit.

7. Its ten-thousandths digit is greater than its hundred-thousandths digit.

8. Its ten-thousandths digit is its first nonzero digit.

9. Two of its digits are odd.

10. Its hundred-thousandths digit is 2.

PUZZLE 29

1. It is a six-digit decimal number.

2. It is greater than $\frac{1}{5}$.

3. It is less than 30%.

4. Each digit is greater than the digit to its left.

5. Its ten-thousandths digit is a multiple of its tenths digit and its hundredths digit.

6. Its tenths digit and its thousandths digit are factors of its hundred-thousandths digit.

7. Only one of its digits is odd.

8. Two of its digits are prime numbers.

9. It is less than 25%.

10. Its hundred-thousandths digit is 8.

PUZZLE 30

1. It is a six-digit decimal number.

2. It is less than $\frac{1}{2}$%.

3. None of its digits are odd.

4. Three of its digits are nonzero.

5. The digit in its smallest place value is divisible by 3.

6. Its thousandths digit is a factor of its ten-thousandths digit.

7. The sum of all of its digits is 14.

8. Its ten-thousandths digit is less than its hundred-thousandths digit.

9. Two of its digits are 4.

10. Its thousandths digit and its ten-thousandths digit are the same.

PUZZLE 31

1. It is a six-digit decimal number.

2. It is less than $\frac{1}{4}$%.

3. It is greater than $\frac{1}{5}$%.

4. Only one of its digits is not divisible by 3.

5. The sum of all of its digits is 11.

6. Its hundred-thousandths digit is its largest digit.

7. The product of its thousandths digit and its ten-thousandths digit is 0.

8. Only two of its digits are nonzero.

9. The difference between its hundred-thousandths digit and its thousandths digit is 7.

10. Its hundred-thousandths digit is 9.

PUZZLE 32

1. It is a five-digit decimal number.

2. Its tenths digit is $\frac{1}{10}$ of its ones digit.

3. It has only two different digits.

4. Its hundreds place value is its largest place value.

5. Its hundredths digit and its hundreds digit are the same.

6. The sum of all of its digits is 6.

7. It is greater than the square of 15.

8. The product of all of its digits is 0.

9. The product of its nonzero digits is 9.

10. Its hundredths digit is 3.

PUZZLE 33

1. It is a five-digit decimal number.

2. It is less than $\frac{7}{2}$.

3. It is greater than $\frac{13}{4}$.

4. The product of all of its digits is 27.

5. Its hundredths digit and its ten-thousandths digit are the same.

6. It has only two different digits.

7. The sum of all of its digits is 11.

8. None of its digits are even.

9. The product of its tenths digit and its thousandths digit is 9.

10. Its hundredths digit is 1.

PUZZLE 34

1. It is a six-digit decimal number.

2. It has only two different digits, each used three times.

3. Its largest place value is its hundreds place.

4. The sum of two of its digits is 1.

5. The quotient of its ones digit and its thousandths digit is 1.

6. The product of any two of its digits is less than 2.

7. The sum of all of its digits is 3.

8. Each of its digits is a square number.

9. It is greater than 101.

10. Its tenths digit is 0.

PUZZLE 35

1. It is a five-digit decimal number.

2. It is less than 100%.

3. Its hundredths digit is 50% of its tenths digit.

4. Its thousandths digit is $33\frac{1}{3}$% of its tenths digit.

5. Its ten-thousandths digit has only one divisor.

6. Only one of its digits is 0.

7. Its tenths digit is a composite number.

8. The sum of its tenths digit and its thousandths digit is twice the sum of its hundredths digit and its ten-thousandths digit.

9. It is less than $\frac{2}{3}$.

10. Its hundredths digit is 3.

PUZZLE 36

1. It is a six-digit decimal number.

2. It is greater than $\frac{17}{8}$.

3. It is less than 225%.

4. The product of all of its digits is 16.

5. Its tenths digit is not its smallest digit.

6. Its hundredths digit and its hundred-thousandths digit are its smallest digits.

7. None of its digits are divisible by 4.

8. The sum of all of its digits is 10.

9. The product of its hundredths digit and its thousandths digit is 2.

10. Its ten-thousandths digit is 2.

PUZZLE 37

1. It is a six-digit decimal number.

2. It is less than 70%.

3. Its tenths digit is $\frac{2}{3}$ of its hundredths digit.

4. Its thousandths digit is $\frac{1}{3}$ of its hundredths digit.

5. The ratio of its ten-thousandths digit to its hundred-thousandths digit is equivalent to 20%.

6. None of its digits are even prime numbers.

7. The product of two of its digits is 5.

8. Its thousandths digit is a divisor of its hundredths digit.

9. Each of its digits is different.

10. Its hundredths digit is 9.

PUZZLE 38

1. It is a seven-digit decimal number.

2. It is less than 1.

3. Its tenths digit is 10% of its hundredths digit.

4. Its thousandths digit is 110% of its ten-thousandths digit.

5. The sum of two of its digits is 1.

6. It has only two different digits.

7. None of its digits are prime numbers.

8. Its hundred-thousandths digit is $\frac{1}{4}$ of its thousandths digit.

9. The sum of all of its digits is 1.

10. Its millionths digit is 1.

PUZZLE 39

1. It is a three-digit decimal number.

2. Its tens digit is a factor of 8.

3. Its tenths digit is a factor of 5.

4. Its ones digit is a cubic number.

5. It has only two different digits.

6. It is greater than the square of 9.

7. The product of its ones digit and its tenths digit is greater than either of those digits.

8. It has more even digits than odd digits.

9. The sum of its digits is greater than 20.

10. Its ones digit is 8.

PUZZLE 40

1. It is a six-digit decimal number.

2. Its ones digit is 25% of its thousandths digit.

3. Its ten-thousandths digit is 25% of its hundred-thousandths digit.

4. Its ones digit and its ten-thousandths digit are the same.

5. Its tenths digit is 1 less than its thousandths digit.

6. Its ones digit is the product of its hundredths digit and its ten-thousandths digit.

7. The sum of three of its digits is 10.

8. It is greater than 200%.

9. Only one of its digits is 1.

10. Its tenths digit is 7.

PUZZLE 41

1. It is a five-digit decimal number.

2. It is greater than 10 but less than 100.

3. The product of two of its digits is 81.

4. The product of its hundredths digit and its thousandths digit is 16.

5. Its ones digit is 50% of its hundredths digit.

6. Its thousandths digit is 100% of its hundredths digit.

7. It has only three different digits.

8. One of its digits is not a square number.

9. The sum of three of its digits is 20.

10. Its ones digit is 2.

PUZZLE 42

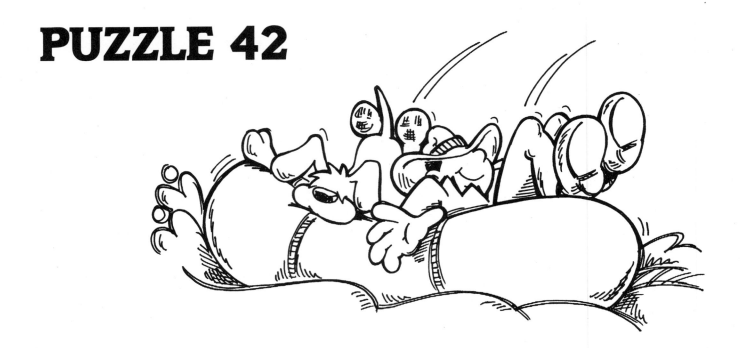

1. It is a five-digit decimal number.

2. Its hundredths digit is not divisible by its hundreds digit.

3. The ratio of its ones digit to its hundredths digit is equivalent to 1:3.

4. It is less than the square of 20.

5. Its tens digit is a factor of both its hundreds digit and its ones digit.

6. Its tenths digit is a factor of its hundredths digit.

7. The sum of three of its digits is 19.

8. Only one of its digits is 1.

9. Three of its digits are square numbers.

10. Its tenths digit is 9.

PUZZLE 43

1. It is a six-digit decimal number.

2. It is greater than $\frac{1}{4}$ but less than $\frac{1}{3}$.

3. Its hundredths digit is its largest digit.

4. Its thousandths digit is $66\frac{2}{3}\%$ of its hundredths digit.

5. Its hundredths digit is the sum of its thousandths digit and its hundred-thousandths digit.

6. Its hundred-thousandths digit is the sum of its tenths digit and its ten-thousandths digit.

7. Two of its digits are composite numbers.

8. One half of its digits are odd.

9. Each of its digits is different.

10. Its thousandths digit is 6.

PUZZLE 44

1. It is a three-digit decimal number.

2. Its hundredths digit is divisible by 4.

3. Its tenths digit is divisible by 3.

4. Its ones digit is divisible by 6.

5. Each of its digits is different.

6. One of its digits is 0.

7. Two of its digits are square numbers.

8. It is greater than 6.25.

9. The difference between two of its digits is 3.

10. Its tenths digit is 9.

PUZZLE 45

1. It is a six-digit decimal number.

2. It has only three different digits, each used twice.

3. The ratio of its tenths digit to its thousandths digit is equivalent to 1:1.

4. The ratio of its ten-thousandths digit to its hundred-thousandths digit is equivalent to 1:1.

5. Its hundredths digit is equal to the difference between its tenths digit and its thousandths digit.

6. The sum of its thousandths digit and its ten-thousandths digit is 8.

7. The product of all of its nonzero digits is 49.

8. It is greater than $\frac{5}{8}$.

9. Its ten-thousandths digit is $\frac{1}{7}$ of its tenths digit.

10. Its hundredths digit is 0.

PUZZLE 46

1. It is a six-digit decimal number.

2. Its hundred-thousandths digit is a divisor of each of its other digits.

3. Its ones digit is neither a prime number nor a composite number.

4. The product of its hundredths digit and its thousandths digit is 49.

5. Its tenths digit is 250% of its ten-thousandths digit.

6. It has five different digits.

7. Four of its digits are prime numbers.

8. Two of its digits are divisible by 5.

9. It is close to 58%.

10. Its ten-thousandths digit is 2.

PUZZLE 47

1. It is a three-digit decimal number.

2. Its hundredths digit is the sum of its ones digit and its tenths digit.

3. Each of its digits is different.

4. None of its digits is a divisor of its other digits.

5. Its ones digit is its smallest digit.

6. Only one of its digits is a prime number.

7. It is greater than 2.99.

8. The difference between two of its digits is 1.

9. Two of its digits are square numbers.

10. Its tenths digit is 5.

PUZZLE 48

1. It is a six-digit decimal number.

2. It is greater than 125% but less than 126%.

3. It has two different pairs of digits that are the same.

4. Its thousandths digit is divisible by 3.

5. Its ten-thousandths digit is divisible by 3.

6. Its hundred-thousandths digit is divisible by 2.

7. Three of its digits are square numbers.

8. Its hundredths digit is not its largest digit.

9. The difference between two of its digits is 7.

10. Two of its digits are 9.

PUZZLE 49

1. It is a five-digit decimal number.

2. Its largest place value is its tens place.

3. The least common multiple of its ones digit and its tenths digit is 9.

4. The least common multiple of its hundredths digit and its thousandths digit is 6.

5. It is less than the square root of 400.

6. None of its digits are prime numbers.

7. The greatest common divisor of its ones digit and its hundredths digit is 3.

8. The product of three of its digits is 1.

9. Only one of its digits is even.

10. Its ones digit is 9.

PUZZLE 50

1. It is a seven-digit decimal number.

2. It is less than 0.1%.

3. Six of its digits are divisible by 9.

4. Five of its digits are divisible by 4.

5. Its hundred-thousandths digit and its millionths digit are the same.

6. The difference between two of its digits is 5.

7. Each of its digits is a square number.

8. It has only three nonzero digits.

9. The product of its ten-thousandths digit and its hundred-thousandths digit is 36.

10. Its millionths digit is 9.

PUZZLE 51

1. It is a four-digit decimal number.

2. Its smallest place value is its thousandths place.

3. It is less than 400% but greater than 100%.

4. Only one of its digits is not a prime number.

5. The difference between its ones digit and its thousandths digit is 3.

6. The product of its prime digits is 105.

7. The product of all of its digits is 0.

8. Its tenths digit is its largest digit.

9. It is greater than 3.7.

10. Its hundredths digit is 5.

PUZZLE 52

1. It is a three-digit decimal number.

2. Its ones digit is a factor of its tenths digit.

3. Its ones digit is not a factor of its hundredths digit.

4. Each of its digits is different.

5. None of its digits are even.

6. It is less than the square root of 16.

7. The sum of its ones digit and its hundredths digit is greater than its tenths digit.

8. Its ones digit is $\frac{1}{3}$ of its tenths digit.

9. Two of its digits are prime numbers.

10. Its hundredths digit is 7.

PUZZLE 53

1. It is an eight-digit decimal number.

2. It is a palindrome.

3. It has only two different digits.

4. The sum of all of its digits is 32.

5. The difference between two of its digits is 4.

6. The sum of its thousands digit and its hundredths digit is 8.

7. The quotient of its ones digit and its tenths digit is 1.

8. The product of its tens digit and its tenths digit is 36.

9. Its thousandths digit is $\frac{1}{3}$ of its tens digit.

10. Its ten-thousandths digit is 2.

PUZZLE 54

1. It is a seven-digit decimal number.

2. It is greater than $\frac{4}{5}$ but less than 1.

3. The ratio of its hundredths digit to its tenths digit is equivalent to 75%.

4. The ratio of its thousandths digit to its tenths digit is equivalent to 75%.

5. Three of its digits are divisible by 5.

6. Its millionths digit is its only odd digit.

7. The product of its hundred-thousandths digit and its millionths digit is not 0.

8. Two of its digits are prime numbers.

9. The quotient of its hundredths digit and its thousandths digit is 1.

10. Its ten-thousandths digit is 0.

Solutions to the Puzzles

The clue number given next to the solution is the first clue in the sequence at which the solution to the puzzle can be determined.

1.	58.102, Clue 7	19.	1.5708, Clue 6	37.	0.69315, Clue 8
2.	0.625, Clue 7	20.	757.727, Clue 7	38.	0.000001, Clue 8
3.	6.039, Clue 7	21.	112.358, Clue 7	39.	88.5, Clue 7
4.	54.5454, Clue 7	22.	1001.0001, Clue 5	40.	2.71828, Clue 7
5.	914.419, Clue 6	23.	861.225, Clue 7	41.	92.944, Clue 6
6.	3.1416, Clue 6	24.	1551.91, Clue 7	42.	213.99, Clue 7
7.	9.1504, Clue 6	25.	555.911, Clue 8	43.	0.29613, Clue 8
8.	1.2480, Clue 5	26.	0.707, Clue 4	44.	6.90, Clue 8
9.	1.3847, Clue 6	27.	102.012, Clue 8	45.	0.70711, Clue 8
10.	99.44, Clue 5	28.	0.000729, Clue 7	46.	0.57721, Clue 6
11.	731.137, Clue 6	29.	0.23468, Clue 6	47.	4.59, Clue 6
12.	3.056, Clue 7	30.	0.00446, Clue 8	48.	1.25992, Clue 8
13.	3.45678, Clue 6	31.	0.00209, Clue 7	49.	19.161, Clue 8
14.	0.8624, Clue 8	32.	300.03, Clue 7	50.	0.000499, Clue 6
15.	0.8088, Clue 7	33.	3.3131, Clue 5	51.	3.750, Clue 8
16.	2.001, Clue 5	34.	101.001, Clue 5	52.	3.97, Clue 7
17.	10.48, Clue 6	35.	0.6321, Clue 6	53.	2266.6622, Clue 8
18.	0.5421, Clue 6	36.	2.21221, Clue 6	54.	0.866025, Clue 8